Abigail

David

Nabal

↑ pronounced NAY-ball

"An often overlooked story retold in a lively, fun way. This book will not only help children remember and retell the events, but also help them apply the important lessons of addressing injustice. A story to inspire young minds and evoke deep discussion."
Joy Vee, children's author

"Abigail, Nabal and David are vividly brought to life with this fun and fabulous book. Abigail is clearly the hero of this story, rising up between two hot-headed men to restore peace and save the lives of her family and friends. The illustrations and rhymes are full of humour and energy. It encourages every girl and boy to trust in the power of God and to stand up for what is good and right."
Joanne Gilchrist, Director of *Ruach Resources* and writer of *God for Kids* app and children's books

"Essential storytelling for the next generation, beautifully written and illustrated. We loved reading it with our little ones!"
Clemmie and Chris ('Harry and Chris') Read

This edition first published in 2022
Text copyright ©Lucy Rycroft
thehopefilledfamily.com

Artwork, book design and layout
©Andy S Gray
onegraydot.com

Printed in the UK.
Hope-Filled Publishing

For my
god-daughter Abigail

This is a story of wisdom and beauty,
Of one clever girl who did more than her duty;
And this is a story of riches and wealth,
Of one man whose stinginess cost him his health.

Abigail lived near Carmel with her clan,
She was married to Nabal – a mean, surly man.
Nabal was rich, yet was foolish in life;
The sense and the wisdom belonged to his wife.

Our story takes place at the time of sheep-shearing –
A time of great feasting, rejoicing and cheering.
All Nabal's shepherds were down in Carmel,
Shearing the sheep for the best wool to sell.

News travels fast, and the news of this fest
Travelled to David, a man who was stressed.
David had looked after Nabal's fine sheep,
Guarding his shepherds while they were asleep.

But now Dave was weary, a man on the run,
Surely this Nabal would give him a bun?

So David announced: "Friends, we protected
All Nabal's possessions – much more than expected.
Well, just as we're growing in need of some tuck
He's having a feast for his friends – what good luck!
Send him my greetings and blessings galore
And surely he'll give us some food from his store."

Ten of them went to seek Nabal's hand,
But Nabal's response was not what they planned.

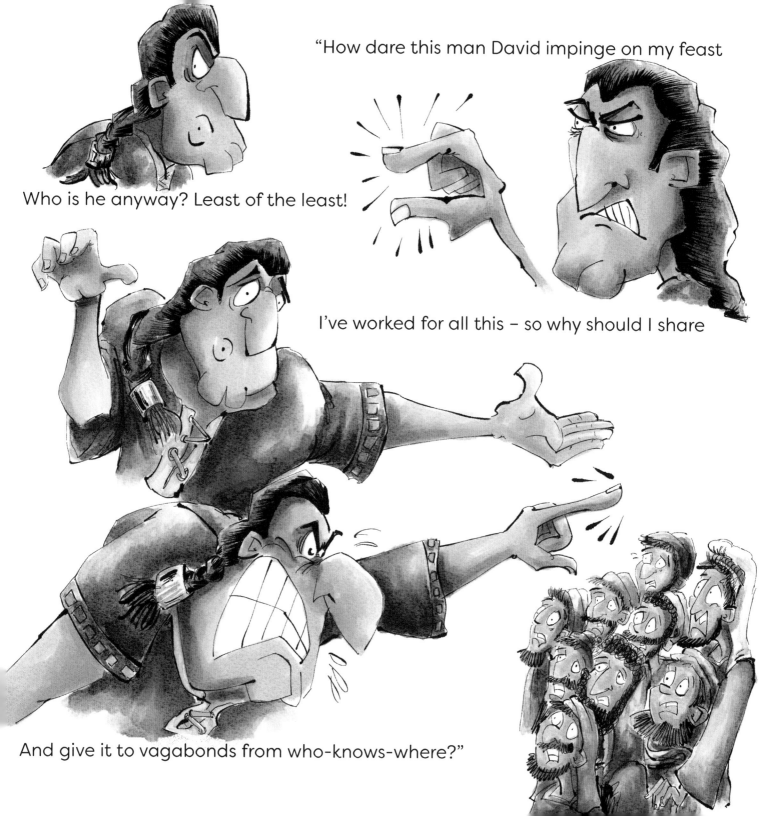

Now nobody wants to be part of a fight,
So David's men turned around, did what was right.
But when they told David how Nabal had roared,
He flew to a rage and he yelled, "Get your sword!
Let's go and find Nabal, we'll make him regret
Not giving us food, not a single baguette!"

Abigail hadn't seen David's men come,
So when she was told that they'd not had a crumb,
She acted in haste to repair the mistake,
And ordered that two hundred loaves should be baked.

Abigail added two skins of good wine
Upon which the men could luxuriously dine;
Plus hundreds of cakes made of raisin and fig,
And five of their sheep who were healthy and big.
Finally, two hundred litres of grain
Were packed on the donkeys, set off on the plain.

Nabal knew nothing of Abigail's pick –
But Abigail knew that she had to act quick.
The lives of her household were all at great risk –
So Abigail knew that she had to be brisk.

Could she, by words, change her family's fate?
Or would she discover they'd acted too late?

David was still in a massive great strop
When Abigail came to suggest he should stop.

She got off her donkey, bowed to the ground,
Fell at his feet and said, while she frowned,
"Master, accept my apology true
My husband's a fool and knows not what to do.
I was not there when you came to our door,
So please, take this choice food and wine from our store

I know that our God will bring blessing to you
He'll make you successful in all that you do.
One day you'll be King, all your battles you'll win –
So don't let your anger lead you to sin."

David stopped short, he put down his sword,
And said, "God has sent you to me – praise the Lord!
If you had not hurried to meet me today
I would have sinned greatly, just as you say.
Thanks for your gift – you have given the best –
So go home in peace – I have heard your request."

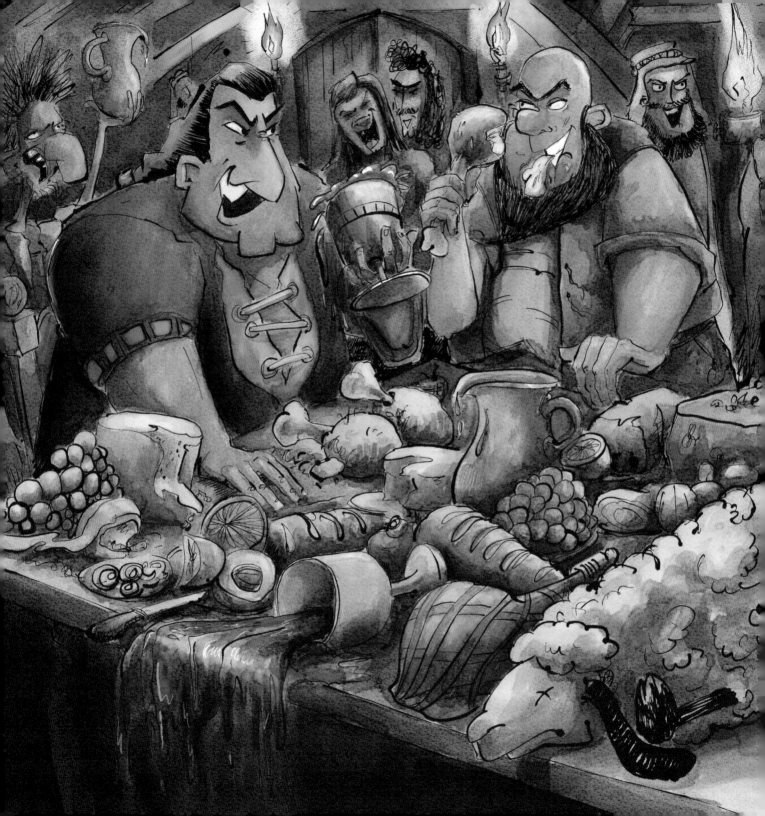

Abi, relieved, set off into the sun,
She went to her husband to tell what she'd done.
But Nabal, who'd said he had no food to share
Was eating and drinking too much – that's not fair!

So when he woke up, the very next morning,
Abigail shared what had passed, gave a warning:
Nabal's behaviour when faced with a stranger
Had put all their servants and shepherds in danger.
Never again must they be under threat.
When Nabal heard this, he started to fret.
His heart went a-flutter, his joints wouldn't bend –
And after ten days, his life came to an end.

David was grateful for Abigail's plea,
So he sent her a message, "Please marry me?"
Abigail thought, "David nearly did wrong,
But then he said sorry to God – that was strong.
I know that our God can forgive anything,
So I'll forgive too, and wear Dave's wedding ring!"

Abigail bowed, and without losing nerve
She said, "I am ready, your people to serve."
She married her David with this certain phrase
And gave him her wisdom for all of her days.

Abigail used her intelligence well
The knock-on effect of her words – who can tell?
Her actions saved many, which helps us to see
That our words have the power to set someone free.

Next time you notice that something's unfair
Remember, like Abigail, you're made to care.
You don't have to worry – you just have to trust
The God that we serve puts His power in us.

About the Author

Lucy Rycroft is the founder of thehopefilledfamily.com, a blog encouraging Christian parents and adopters. You can also find her on Instagram @thehopefilledfamily where she offers regular encouragement. Lucy lives in York, UK with her husband, four children and a crazy cockapoo called Monty.

Receive Lucy's free Christian parenting encouragement every Friday, plus win books and grab free downloads by signing up for her emails at thehopefilledfamily.com

About the illustrator

Andy S. Gray is illustrator of the award winning *Whistlestop Tales*, and many other titles over the last 20 years. He's also a Church of England minister. He's worked professionally with children and young people for over 30 years in schools and churches.

He is proud to be autistic, and encourages people to embrace their uniquness and live life to the full.

You can see more of his work at www.onegraydot.com and on instagram @onegraydot.

Did you know . . ?

You can read the original story of Abigail,
Nabal and David in 1 Samuel 25 in any Bible, or
at biblegateway.com

Collect the set!

Deborah and Jael

Look out for more Mighty Girl, Mighty God books - coming soon!

Printed in Great Britain
by Amazon